Chihuly Art Kit
Activity Book

Let's get started!

Most of the art projects in this book are easy to create, but require the help of an adult. Take special caution with the projects that involve scissors and use of the microwave. Before you get started with any activity, lay down newspaper or a towel to protect your work surface. When you are finished, and you have created your masterpieces, don't forget to clean up. Tidy the area by putting away your crayons, paints, pencils, or extra paper, and make sure to wash all your paintbrushes. On the next page is a list of all materials you will need to do the art projects. Now gather your materials and get creative!

Projects

Marshmallow Madness — Page 14
materials needed: An adult to help you, 1 large marshmallow, 1 plate, a microwave

Colored Pencil Craziness — Page 20
materials needed: a blank page from this book or a big piece of paper, as many colored pencils as you want

Colors Compounded! — Page 26
materials needed: newspaper to protect your work surface, a blank page from this book or a big piece of paper, watercolor paint—as many different colors as you can find

Wonderful Weaving — Page 32
materials needed: paper from the back of this book to cut into strips to weave, transparent tape or glue, an empty canister (soda or coffee can)

Sea Creature Creation — Page 38
materials needed: newspaper to protect your work surface, a blank page from this book or a big piece of paper, pieces of fruit or vegetables (apples, oranges, potatoes), paint (tempera is best), empty plastic containers

Color Collage — Page 44
materials needed: a blank page from this book or a big piece of paper, colored paper from the back of this book, a glue stick

Tackling Texture — Page 50
materials needed: newspaper to protect your work surface; a blank page from this book or a big piece of paper; things with an interesting surface—sandpaper, cloth, wood, rice, beans, or household items like cardboard; colored pencils, crayons, pencils, or paints

Chandelier Challenge and Tower Trouble — Page 56
materials needed: newspaper to protect your work surface, play dough, toothpicks, an apple, pear, or potato

Itty Bitty Ice Wall — Page 62
materials needed: ice cubes, a baking sheet, a small towel

Sticker Garden Surprise — Page 68
materials needed: a blank page from this book or a big piece of paper, colored pencils, crayons, or paints, stickers (you can find some in the back of this book)

Stickers — Page 75

Colored paper — Page 79

Dale Chihuly (chih-WHO-lee) is an artist who creates his work out of glass. He also draws and paints. Chihuly has created hundreds of projects using glass, some as tall as an evergreen tree, some that float, and even one that weighs over 40,000 pounds. Some projects are so big that they take over thirty people just to put them together.

Chihuly was born in Tacoma, Washington, in 1941. When he was in school, he first studied design and later went on to blow glass, paint, and even make sculptures out of ice! During his life, he has taught, set up art exhibits, and worked with artists from around the world. In this book, we'll tell you about how Chihuly and his team create amazing pieces of art. Follow along to learn about the inspiration for some of his ideas. Then you can try the activities and put these ideas into action!

In order to create his colorful pieces, Chihuly uses hot glass. Glassblowing requires unique equipment and a whole team of specially trained adults. This ancient process is not something you can do at home. To shape glass, you have to work in a hotshop where a 2,150°F furnace holds liquid glass and special ovens allow pieces to cool. First, a mixture of sand or quartz and other materials is placed into a furnace where it is melted. The artist uses a piece of constantly rotating steel pipe to "gather" the glass. The glassblower then blows into the pipe, creating a bubble of liquid glass at the end. Next, wooden paddles and blocks are used to shape the bubble. Moving the glass back and forth between two furnaces, the artist forms his piece. The glass is dangerously hot—certainly too hot to touch—so sometimes water-soaked newspaper is pressed against the bubble, sending steam into the room. When the piece is complete, it is moved to a specialized oven, called an annealer, to cool slowly for many hours or even days. Quick changes in temperature would cause the glass to crack. Chihuly was in college when he started blowing glass, and he'll never forget his first bubble.

People have been blowing glass since the first century BC—over 2,100 years ago! In ancient times, glass was made from sand, plant ash, and lime. Today it is made mostly with sand or quartz and other materials.

Tidbits

Activity:

To use the common household marshmallow to pretend to blow glass. A marshmallow is like glass because it becomes soft and gooey when heated. Like a glassblower, you have to work quickly to shape the warm, soft marshmallow before it solidifies.

Supplies:

An adult to help you
1 large marshmallow
1 plate
A microwave

Steps:

1. Place the marshmallow on a plate. Have an adult microwave it on high for thirty seconds.
2. Be careful—the marshmallow will be very hot! Allow it to cool down until it is safe to touch. Ask an adult to check the temperature before you touch it yourself.
3. Pull the warm marshmallow apart to make wild, stretchy shapes.

Bonus Bubble:

In his Reeds, Chihuly stretches one single piece of glass as far as seven feet. How far can you stretch one marshmallow before it breaks? Try twisting two, three, or more marshmallows together. Can you make them into plants, trees, or creatures?

Dale's travels

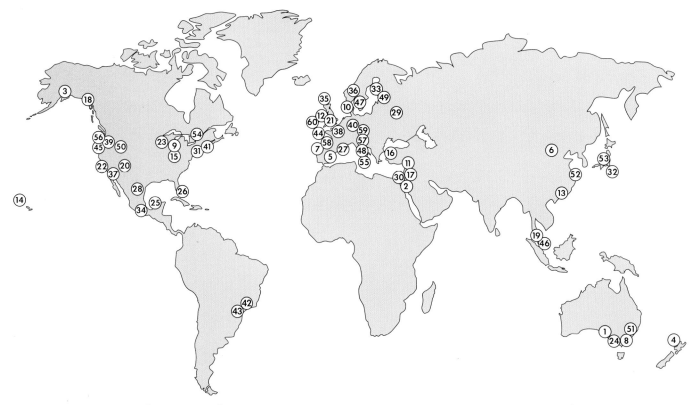

1. Adelaide, Australia
2. Amman, Jordan
3. Anchorage, Alaska, United States
4. Auckland, New Zealand
5. Barcelona, Spain
6. Beijing, China
7. Bilbao, Spain
8. Canberra, Australia
9. Chicago, Illinois, United States
10. Copenhagen, Denmark
11. Damascus, Syria
12. Dublin, Ireland
13. Hong Kong, China
14. Honolulu, Hawaii, United States
15. Indianapolis, Indiana, United States
16. Istanbul, Turkey
17. Jerusalem, Israel
18. Juneau, Alaska, United States
19. Kuala Lumpur, Malaysia
20. Las Vegas, Nevada, United States
21. London, United Kingdom
22. Los Angeles, California, United States
23. Madison, Wisconsin, United States
24. Melbourne, Australia
25. Merida, Mexico
26. Miami, Florida, United States
27. Monte Carlo, Monaco
28. Monterrey, Mexico
29. Moscow, Russia
30. Negev Desert, Israel
31. New York, New York, United States
32. Niijima, Japan
33. Nuutajärvi, Finland
34. Oaxaca, Mexico
35. Orkney Islands, Scotland
36. Oslo, Norway
37. Palm Springs, California, United States
38. Paris, France
39. Pilchuck, Washington, United States
40. Prague, Czech Republic
41. Providence, Rhode Island, United States
42. Rio de Janeiro, Brazil
43. Sao Paulo, Brazil
44. Scilly Islands, United Kingdom
45. Seattle, Washington, United States
46. Singapore
47. Smaland, Sweden
48. Spoleto, Italy
49. St. Petersburg, Russia
50. Sun Valley, Idaho, United States
51. Sydney, Australia
52. Taipei, Taiwan
53. Tokyo, Japan
54. Toronto, Canada
55. Valletta, Malta
56. Vancouver, Canada
57. Venice, Italy
58. Vianne, France
59. Vienna, Austria
60. Waterford, Ireland

During the 1960s and 1970s, Chihuly traveled the world teaching art and learning new skills. He traveled to Jordan and Russia, Sweden and Czechoslovakia, and around the United States. Throughout his travels, he studied art and techniques that he uses today in his artwork. Chihuly was influenced by many things he saw, including the Native American woven baskets of the Northwest Coast, the glassblowers in Italy, and the art of Ikebana (flower arranging) from Japan. If you look closely at his *Blanket Cylinders*, for example, you can see elements of Native American blanket designs. Or looking at his gardens of glass, you may find influences from artisans in Japan. Chihuly loves to travel, and he blows his adventures into his art. You need only look closely to see the rich cultures and travels reflected in his colorful pieces.

Ikebana is the traditional Japanese art of arranging flowers. For over 600 years, artisans have carefully placed flowers in these planned arrangements, where even the petals are considered a part of the sculpture-like art.

Tidbits

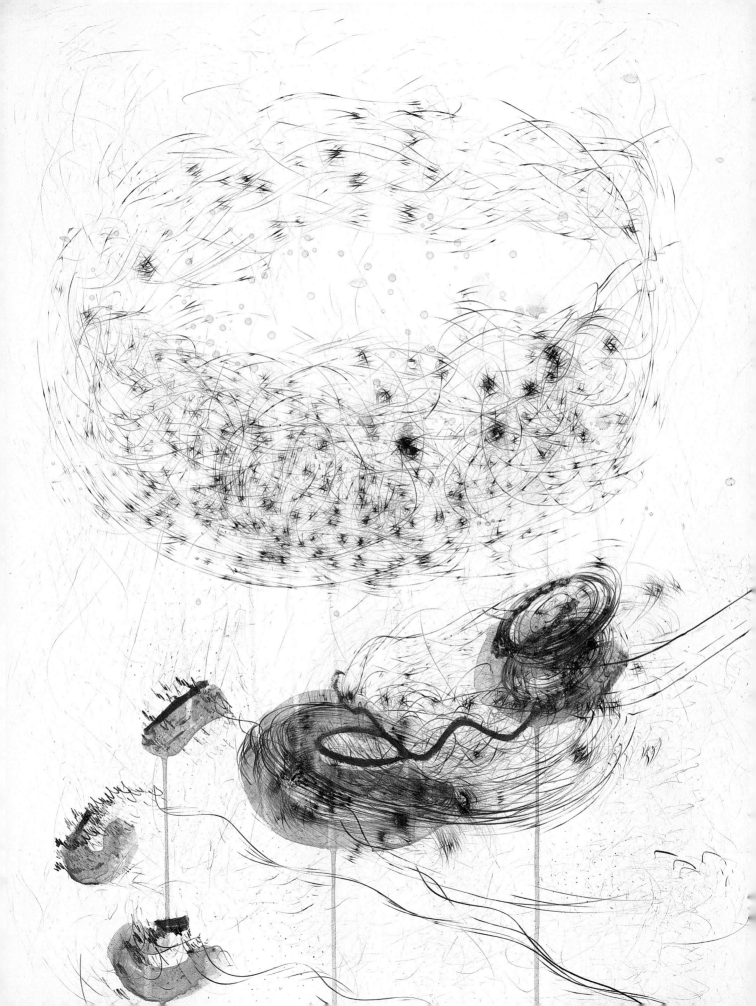

Chihuly is known mostly for his glass artwork, but he also loves to draw. One day, he picked up a whole handful of colored pencils, as many as he could fit in his hand. Then, with the huge handful of pencils, he drew on a big sheet of paper. The shapes he drew looked as if they were moving in the air. These shapes, with all their lines, are bursting with energy. Chihuly likes to create drawings that are fluid and that don't follow any rules. Chihuly's mother looked at these pictures and shook her head; she didn't understand what he was doing. But Chihuly continued to draw, putting his creativity into these swirling, colorful shapes on the page. Chihuly often gets energy and inspiration from the whirling designs he creates with simple colored pencils.

"I don't know anyone who has as much fun drawing as I do," says Chihuly.

Tidbits

In ancient times, a thin stick of lead called a stylus was used to write. Today most pencils actually contain graphite, which came into use in the 1500s. Because graphite is so delicate, pencil makers came up with the idea to put the graphite into a wooden shell to protect it.

Activity:
Make your own big-handful-of-pencils drawing.

Supplies:
The next page of this book or a big piece of paper
As many colored pencils as you want

Steps:
1. Pick up a whole handful of pencils. If there are too many for you to hold easily, use rubber bands around the top and bottom of the pencil bundle to keep them together.
2. Draw any shapes that come to mind. You may want to try circles, squares, spirals, straight lines, people, or animals.

What do you see? Does the object look as if it is moving? Does it still look like the original object, or does it now look like something else?

Bonus Bubble:
Use crayons, pens, markers, or other drawing tools the same way, or mix and match them. Now draw the same object using similar colors (like using all reds). How does that change the picture? Is it easier to see the object you are drawing? What happens when you use fewer pencils or crayons? Does it still look as if it is moving? How do your pictures differ?

One day, after sitting for hours on a train traveling across Canada, Chihuly decided to play with his paints. He mixed up his watercolors to see how many new colors he could make. He made swatches, or samples on pieces of paper, of every color he could imagine. By the time he got off the train, he had made about 2,000 swatches.

When Chihuly started blowing glass, most finished pieces had only one or two colors in them, but Chihuly loves color, and he's not afraid to experiment. He used the swatches of colors from the train and the newfound strange combinations of colors in his art. He loves color so much that sometimes, he even tries to use as many colors as possible in one piece or one series of art.

"I'm obsessed with color," Chihuly admits. "Never saw one I didn't like."

Tidbits

Colors Compounded!

Activity:

Use paint to mix, match, and create new colors.

Supplies:

Newspaper to cover your work surface
The next page of this book or a big piece of paper
Watercolor paint—as many different colors as you can find

Steps:

1. Put newspaper down on the table or work surface to protect it from paint.
2. Try painting stripes of color next to each other on a sheet of paper.
3. Look at the colors and imagine what they would turn into if you mixed them.
4. Next, mix the colors in two ways:
   a. Paint one color on top of another one on your paper to see how they blend.
   b. Mix some of your different paints together in a bowl and then paint your new color onto the paper. Don't be afraid to try strange combinations.
5. Choose your favorite combinations of colors, and paint a design using your new colors and your original colors.

Bonus Bubble:

Try this activity with tempera or other types of paint. Sometimes mixing lots of colors means you end up with globs of brown paint. Don't worry—the color brown can be interesting. Sometimes mistakes make the best art! Can you mix shades that look like the color of a tree trunk, the dirt in your backyard, or your mom's cup of coffee?

Chihuly makes a series of artwork that he calls *Blanket Cylinders*. He and his team worked together to come up with the idea to make "drawings" out of very thin threads of glass and melt the drawing into the glass, which was then shaped into a cylinder.

To create these, Chihuly and his team lay hundreds of different-colored strands of glass—each strand is almost as thin as a piece of hair—on a metal table. To create the drawing, they arrange all these tiny pieces together in a woven pattern. After blowing a big glass bubble, they pick up the glass threads or drawing, rolling it onto the side of the glass bubble. As the bubble is blown, it is shaped into a cylinder. While it is being blown, the design stretches and changes shape. This drawing then becomes a part of the cylinder. When the glass has cooled, and the piece is finished, you can see the drawing—sometimes twisted and stretched— within it. This "weaving" style is similar to the beautiful Native American woven blankets Chihuly saw on his travels. It's amazing to think that a soft piece of fabric can inspire a hard, smooth piece of glass art.

For many Native Americans, blankets are much more than bed covers. Native Americans use woven blankets as gifts at birthdays and weddings, to pay debts, as temporary shelters in the rain or cold, as curtains, as a warm cover, as clothing, or to swaddle babies.

Tidbits

Wonderful Weaving

Activity:

Use paper to weave and create your own "woven cylinder."

Supplies:

Paper from the back of this book to cut into strips to weave
Transparent tape or glue
An empty canister (soda or coffee can)

Steps:

1. Cut at least ten strips of paper all the same width. One-inch strips work well.
2. Tape the tops of five of the strips to a piece of paper to hold them in place.
3. Use the other five strips to weave in and out as the illustration shows.
4. When you are done weaving, remove the tape from the top of the paper. Then tape or glue the entire weaving to the can.
5. Try cutting more strips and weaving larger blankets.

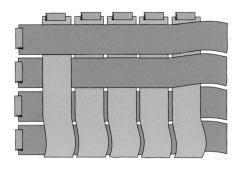 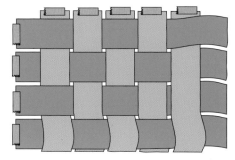

Bonus Bubble:

Instead of using paper, try making your strips out of tinfoil, cloth, ribbon, newspaper, or other materials. Experiment with strips of different sizes. In Step 1, create 1-inch wide, half-inch wide, or various-sized strips. Instead of gluing your finished woven blanket onto a canister, try affixing it to another object to display it—a box, a notebook, or a paper cup.

Chihuly strives to make shapes of glass that no one has ever seen before. Some of his glass looks like imaginary undersea animals or plants. Chihuly has always loved to go to the beach and look at the ocean. He's even worked on the sea, in Alaska, as a fisherman. His fascination with glass may have started when, as a child, he found pieces of sand-polished glass, or sea glass, as he walked along the shore of the Pacific Ocean. So, sure enough, without even realizing it, as Chihuly blew glass, his pieces evolved to look like sea forms: shells, jellyfish, and urchins. Their many colors are bright like tropical fish and the edges are wavy and delicate. The glass pieces look as if they are sitting on the seafloor, swaying with the current. Which sea creatures can you see in the piece on the opposite page?

Sea Creature Creation

Activity:

To create a picture of an unusual, exotic, completely made-up ocean animal.

Supplies:

Newspaper to cover your work surface
The next page of this book or a big piece of paper
Pieces of fruit or vegetables (apples, oranges, potatoes)
Paint (tempera is best)
Empty plastic containers

Steps:

1. Put newspaper down on the table or work surface to protect it from paint.
2. Ask an adult to cut each piece of fruit or vegetable so that there is one flat side. You will use this side like a stamp.
3. Once you have a collection of stamp shapes, put several colors of paint into the empty plastic containers.
4. Dip the stamps into the paint.
5. Using the colors and your stamps, try to create something that looks as if it might live deep in the ocean or on a different planet. Use your imagination! What would you name your creature? Where does it live?

Bonus Bubble:
Use a sponge, a wad of paper, or plastic wrap to create stamps.

Chihuly woke up one morning and said, "I'm going to use all 300 colors of glass that are made, in as many combinations as I can." He called this new series of artworks *Macchia* (MAH-key-ah), which is Italian for "spotted."

For these pieces, Chihuly mixed up all the colors in different ways, like a collage, to create all sorts of multicolored, spotted *Macchia*. With so many colors, some people thought his new creations were ugly at first, but Chihuly loved them and kept on making them. Today they are displayed in museums around the world. Can you count the number of colors in the one on the opposite page?

Activity:

Make a paper collage using every color you can imagine. *Macchia* spots are created by melting many small bits of color onto a piece of glass. With that same idea, you will attach many small bits of color to one piece of paper.

Supplies:

Newspaper to cover your work surface
The next page of this book or a big piece of paper
Colored paper from the back of this book
A glue stick

Steps:

1. Put newspaper down on the table or work surface to protect it.
2. Cut or rip the colored paper into pieces. Try making lots of different shapes in lots of different sizes.
3. Use your glue stick to glue the bits to a sheet of paper. You can make it look like something you've seen before, like a plant or animal, or make something that makes no sense at all.

Bonus Bubble:
Instead of plain paper, use foil, plastic, paper bags, tissue paper, newspaper, wrapping paper, etc.

Most glass is smooth if you run your hand over it. Sometimes Chihuly's glass has long lines or round circles of color that look bumpy, even if they feel smooth. This is because Chihuly puts lots of different kinds of color onto one piece of glass, sometimes in long, thin threads and sometimes in big, rough chunks. The colored glass melts, but it leaves behind the appearance of a line or a bump.

Glassblowing is difficult, because in creating it you have to get the extreme temperatures just right. If the glass is too hot, it will lose its shape and become floppy. If the glass is too cool, it will crack or shatter. By heating and reheating pieces at exactly the right moment, artists can mold and shape the glass into different forms. Chihuly likes to experiment with glass as it transforms from the molten glowing red bubble, to see what shapes and textures he can create.

Tackling Texture

Activity:

Use textures to make an individual piece of art.

Supplies:

Newspaper to cover your work surface
The next page of this book or a big piece of paper
Things with an interesting surface—sandpaper, cloth, wood, rice, beans, or household items like cardboard
Colored pencils, crayons, pencils, or paints

Steps:

1. Put newspaper down on the table or work surface to protect it.
2. Put your textured items under your sheet of paper and hold them down together with one hand.
3. With the other hand, color or draw on the paper. The texture underneath the paper will show through. It might make your pencil go in weird directions, but that's part of the effect of the texture. The less you press on the paper, the more the pencil will glide over the bumps.
4. Try coloring in a solid area, using your pencils or markers or crayons. The various types of supplies will make your textures look different.

What do your drawings look like? Do they look like animal skin, with spots or scales or stripes? Do you see how, even though the flat paper is smooth, it looks bumpy—just like Chihuly's pieces?

Bonus Bubble:

Add these new rubbings into your Color Collage or your Wonderful Weaving projects.

Chihuly tries to create things that other people say are impossible to build. One thing he likes to do is make huge glass sculptures called *Chandeliers* and *Towers* and put them in interesting places. He has built these in Italy, Israel, and many other countries.

These structures start out as hundreds or even thousands of individual pieces of glass. Then the glass pieces are attached to enormous metal structures that look like steel skeletons. From the outside, no one would ever guess there is so much metal inside! Instead, like a bunch of grapes, it looks as if the pieces are just hung together without a stem. It takes many people to create one of these beautiful sculptures from start to finish. For example, for the *Chihuly Over Venice* project, Chihuly worked with glass factories and artisans from around the world to make *Chandeliers*. These enormous glass sculptures were brought to Venice, assembled from all their many pieces, and hung on display over the canals.

Venice is a city in Italy with waterways throughout instead of roads. There are very few cars there and instead people travel by boat or by walking across bridges that connect the buildings.

Tidbits

Chandelier Challenge and Tower Trouble

Activity:

Use play dough (store bought, or make your own following the instructions in the Bonus Bubble) to create a *Chandelier* or *Tower*.

Supplies:

Newspaper to cover your work surface
Play dough
Toothpicks
An apple, pear, or potato

Tower Steps:

1. Put newspaper down on the table or work surface to protect it.
2. Separate your dough into small pieces, under an inch square. Try making them all the same shape, or try different sizes.
3. Stack the pieces of play dough into the shape of a tower. How high can you stack them?

Chandelier Steps:

1. Ready to try making a support structure? Poke one toothpick into each dough shape of your *Tower*.
2. Using the fruit, or potato, push each toothpick with a dough shape on it into the fruit wherever you want it. Now you have a *Chandelier*!

Bonus Bubble:

To make your own play dough, mix together the following:
1 cup flour, 1 cup water, 1 cup salt,
1 tablespoon cream of tartar, food coloring (optional).

Chihuly doesn't work only with glass and paint—he also works with ice! Chihuly likes ice because, like glass, ice changes shape at different temperatures and is transparent, meaning you can see through it. One time, Chihuly put sixteen glass sculptures in an ancient fortress in Jerusalem, Israel. Then he had sixty-four tons of ice blocks shipped to Jerusalem all the way from Alaska. The huge blocks arrived and soon began to melt under the hot Israeli sun. Chihuly and his team worked fast to build a large wall of ice outside the fortress walls, right next to a major road where everyone could see it. Brightly colored lights lit up the melting ice at night, making it look mysterious and wonderful.

While this cool artwork lasted only three days, Chihuly still thought it was important to construct because it symbolized the melting of tensions between the Middle East and the West and it drew lots of attention to this special place.

Chihuly used twenty-four blocks of Alaskan Arctic Diamond ice to build this ice wall. Each piece of ice weighed close to 5,000 pounds. All the ice traveled by ship in a special refrigerator container. That's almost 6,000 miles.

Tidbits

Itty Bitty Ice Wall

Activity:

You can't build an ice wall in an ancient fortress in Israel, but you can attempt to build a little one in your kitchen to see how difficult it is to work with melting ice!

Supplies:

Ice cubes
A baking sheet
A small towel

Steps:

1. Make your ice cubes.
2. Once the cubes are frozen, put a towel on a baking sheet to use as a work surface.
3. Dump the ice cubes onto the towel that's on the baking sheet.
4. Build a tall wall, a pyramid, or a fortress. Are the cubes slippery? Think about how you can position the cubes to support each other. Can you place the cubes around another piece of art you have created like the Wonderful Weaving or Color Collage?

Bonus Bubble:

Make your ice cubes different colors, using food coloring. Add a drop or two of food coloring to each cube before you freeze them. Make sure no one you live with will mind if you put the different-colored ice cubes on the towel—the ice cubes might stain it. Before the ice cubes melt all the way, try using them to draw pictures. The food coloring should make these ice cubes work like watercolor paints!

Chihuly loves to surprise people by putting glass in unexpected places. Most artists put their artwork in museums or galleries, but one of Chihuly's favorite things to do is display his artwork in nature.

He likes to visit botanical gardens and put *Towers* and *Chandeliers* inside glasshouses that are filled with palm trees or ferns. Then he places some glass among the flowers, and lets other pieces drift on lily ponds. A lot of what Chihuly creates looks as if it could come from nature, so the glass and the gardens seem to fit together.

Glasshouses, also called greenhouses, are buildings made almost entirely of windows that, because of the sunlight, have an interior temperature ideal for growing plants and flowers.

Tidbits

Sticker Garden Surprise

Activity:
Create a garden and then use stickers to create a "glass garden."

Supplies:
The next page of this book or a big piece of paper
Colored pencils, crayons, or paints
Stickers (you can find some in the back of this book)

Steps:
1. Using your art supplies, draw a big garden filled with trees and flowers. Add a pond or palm trees. What kind of plants are your favorite? Add them to your garden.
2. Find the sheet of stickers at the back of this book.
3. Now, design your own glass garden by placing the stickers on your drawing. What "glass" would look good in your garden?

Bonus Bubble:
In your yard or in a potted plant, add items to create a new garden scene. Add small cans, marbles, pencils, toys, or other objects. Try to make some of the items camouflaged (or blended into the plant) and others stand out like a bright flower. What would you name your new plants or flowers?

Chihuly dreams up many different shapes and techniques for making artwork. He and his team are always working to discover new ideas. Now that you've completed the activities in this book, you can go back and create them again and again. Try using different materials, surfaces, pieces of fruit, colors, etc. No two pieces of art will ever be exactly alike. Continue to come up with new ideas every day. Use your imagination— experiment and create!

Colophon

This second printing of the
Chihuly Art Kit Activity Book
is limited to 4,000 copies.
The entire contents are copyright © 2006
Dale Chihuly. All rights reserved.

Photography Team Jan Cook, David Emery, Claire Garoutte,
Nick Gunderson, Russell Johnson, Robin Kimmerling,
Scott M. Leen, Teresa N. Rishel, Terry Rishel, and Rob Whitworth

Writing Team Kristin Buzzelli, Jamie Holland, Erica Jacobs,
Julianna Ross, and Joanna Sikes

Design Team Anna Katherine Curfman and Barry Rosen

Project Development Team Kristin Buzzelli, Diane Caillier,
Ken Clark, Sadie Crowe, Anna Katherine Curfman,
Jamie Daniels, Nicole Hammill, Jamie Holland, Paula Jacobson,
Jennifer Lewis, Julianna Ross, and Piper Ross

Typefaces Futura and Schoolbook
Paper Lumisilk matt art 150 gsm

Printing and manufacturing Global PSD, China

Portland Press
PO Box 70856, Seattle, Washington 98127
800 574 7272
www.portlandpress.net

ISBN-13: 978-1-57684-171-6
ISBN-10: 1-57684-171-5

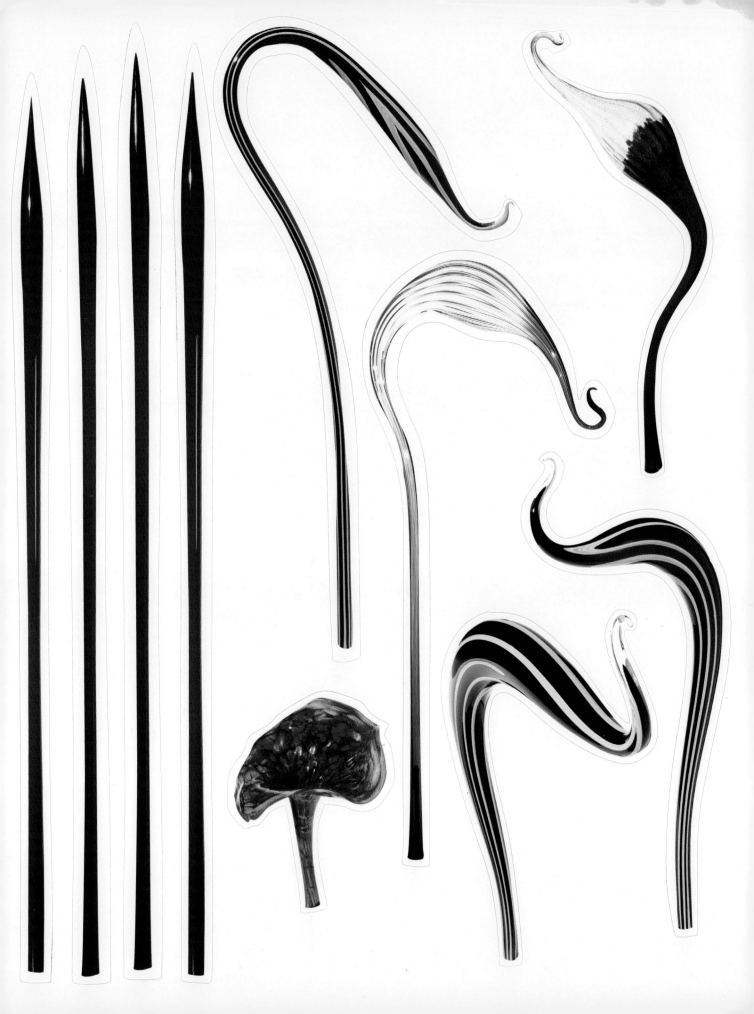

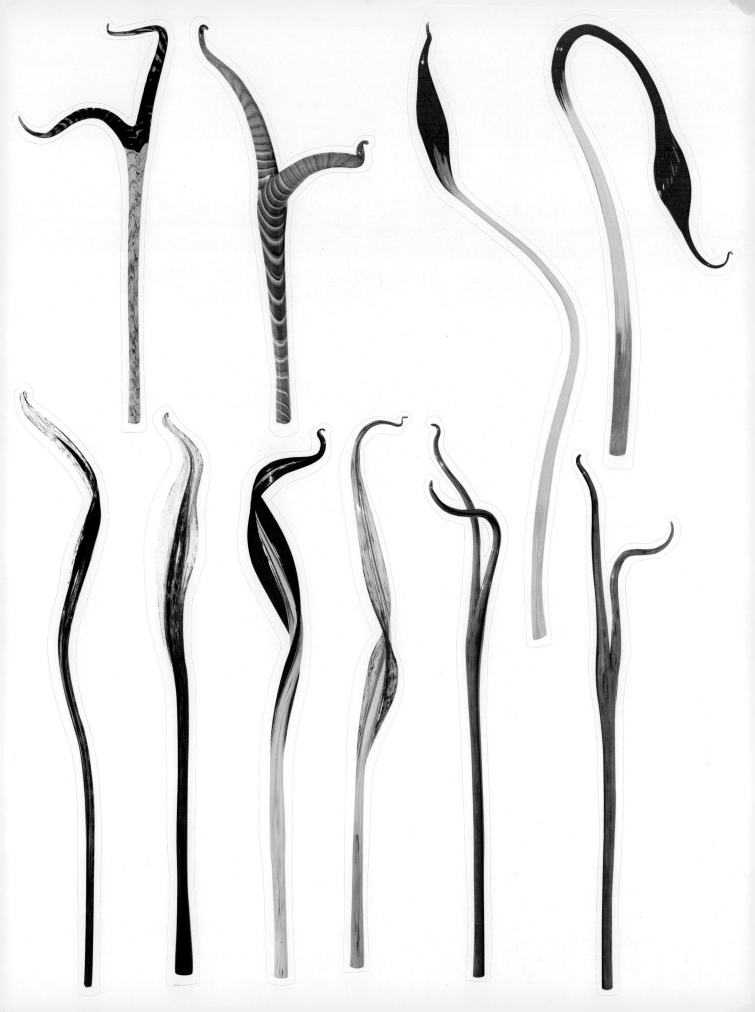